Stevie Ingram-Palmer

Poppy the **Pa**rrot

BROWN
DOG
BOOKS

A CIP catalogue record for this title is available from the British Library.

Published under licence by Brown Dog Books and The Self-Publishing Partnership Ltd. 10b Greenway Farm, Bath Rd, Wick, nr. Bath, BS30 5RL.

ISBN: 978-1-83952-733-3

Cover and internal design by Stevie Ingram-Palmer

Printed and bound in Great Britain

This book is printed on FSC®certified paper.

The intellectual property of Bionic Reading® is based on Patent, Trademark and Copyright Laws. Bionic Reading® AG is an authorized partner of BRCG Casutt GmbH and develops, distributes and commercializes the Bionic Reading® products. BRCG Casutt GmbH, Masanserstrasse 194, CH-7000 Chur, Switzerland, is the exclusive rights holder of Bionic Reading®.

The copyright holder of this book is an authorized partner and licensee of the reading method "Bionic Reading®" and has defined the following Bionic Reading® settings.
Fixation: 3
Saccade: 10
Part of speech: "Yes" for all types of words
Letters or Syllables: "Letters"

More about Bionic Reading®
bionic-reading.com

Dedication

This book **i**s dedicated **t**o anyone **w**ho finds **the**mselves easily **dis**tracted, struggles **t**o concentrate **o**r who **expe**riences periods **o**f hyperactivity, (**wh**ether through **AD**HD or **f**or any **ot**her reason).

I hope **th**is book **gi**ves you a main **cha**racter you **c**an relate **t**o, and **mo**st importantly a feeling **of** happiness!

I also **ho**pe it **c**an be **us**ed to **st**art a **conv**ersation with **all** children **ab**out diversity **a**nd inclusion **a**nd as a tool **t**o celebrate **t**he different **tr**aits that **ma**ke us **all** special!

♥

Poppy the **pa**rrot loves **to** squark **and** to **si**ng.

To dance **wi**th her **le**gs and **to** wave **wi**th her **wi**ngs.

It feels **re**ally good **mo**ving around.

Fluffing her **fea**thers, or **ta**pping the **gr**ound.

One day **in** the **su**mmer she **es**caped from **h**er cage,

She flew **in**to the **ga**rden in **an** excited **da**ze.

She flew **re**ally fast **u**p into **t**he air,

over the **ga**rdens and **th**rough a **f**un fair.

She flew **and** she **fl**ew... then **s**he flew **so**me more!

For hours **and** hours, **un**til she **g**ot bored.

Then she **de**cided it **w**as time **to** go **ho**me,

but she **lo**oked around **and** realised **h**ow far **s**he had **fl**own.

Suddenly Poppy **fe**lt lonely **a**nd scared.

She didn't **kn**ow where **s**he was, **s**he didn't **kn**ow who **ca**red.

Poppy's feelings **a**re always **o**n show,

so you **w**on't have **t**o guess - you'll **al**ways know.

Anger, sadness, **exc**itement, joy.

She keeps **h**er feelings **o**n show **a**nd doesn't **pl**ay coy!

She was **cr**ying when **s**he met a parrot **ca**lled Pat,

Pat helped **d**ry her **te**ars and **pa**tted her **ba**ck.

"I **kn**ow the **w**ay home" **P**at declared,

"**b**ut you **mu**st make **m**e a **pr**omise before I take **y**ou there".

Poppy the **pa**rrot let **o**ut a **sn**iff,

"I'll make **y**ou a **pr**omise – **any**thing you **wi**sh!"

"**Al**ways keep **yo**ur heart **o**f gold,
stay funny **and** happy **and** clever **and** bold".

Poppy nodded **her** head, **ha**ppy not **to** be **al**one,
and her **n**ew friend **P**at, flew **her** straight **ho**me.

Poppy the **Pa**rrot
PARENT AND CARER'S GUIDE

The best **w**ay to **g**et a **ch**ild with **AD**HD engaged **i**n an **act**ivity is **in**stant gratification!! **Chi**ldren with **AD**HD will **n**ot often **ha**ve the **att**ention span **t**o stick **at** something **wi**th a **lo**nger term **p**ay off - so **ma**king it **ins**tantly enjoyable **i**s key!

With that **in** mind, **he**re are **so**me tips **f**or helping **yo**ur child **wi**th ADHD **en**gage with **bo**oks!

Involve them **in** the **wh**ole experience!

1. **In**volve them **in** the **pr**ocess before **y**ou've even **pi**cked the **bo**ok up, **ma**ybe visit a library **o**r book **sh**op and **al**low them **t**o look **f**or and **fe**el the **bo**oks which **a**re most **app**ealing to **th**em. This **wi**ll be **a**n enjoyable **act**ivity, and **i**t will **bu**ild anticipation **f**or you **t**o read **t**he book **tog**ether... giving **a**n instant **p**ay off **fr**om the **mo**ment you **tu**rn that **fi**rst page!

2. **Le**t them **ch**oose the **bo**ok! If **i**t seems **t**oo young **f**or them, **d**on't worry! **All**owing them **t**o choose the book **f**or themselves **wi**ll again **bu**ild the **exc**itement of **re**ading it **f**or them. **Th**e important **th**ing is **th**at you **a**re building a love **of** books **fr**om a **yo**ung age.

3. **Fi**nd a **sel**ection with **to**pics they **li**ke or **c**an relate **t**o. Do **th**ey have a special **int**erest? Maybe **sp**orts, art **o**r animals? **Wha**tever it **is**, try **t**o find a selection **o**f books **o**n the **to**pic they **c**an pick **fr**om. This **wi**ll help **ke**ep them **en**gaged for **th**at bit **lo**nger.

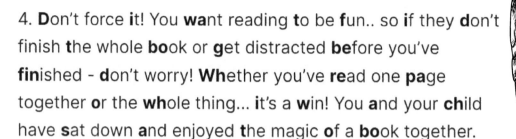

4. **D**on't force **i**t! You **wa**nt reading **t**o be **f**un.. so **if** they **d**on't finish **t**he whole **bo**ok or **g**et distracted **be**fore you've **fin**ished - **d**on't worry! **Wh**ether you've **re**ad one **pa**ge together **o**r the **wh**ole thing... **it**'s a **w**in! You **a**nd your **ch**ild have **s**at down **a**nd enjoyed **t**he magic **o**f a **bo**ok together.

Poppy the **Pa**rrot
PARENT AND **CA**RER'S GUIDE

I **al**so wanted **t**o include **so**me practical **ti**ps for **man**aging ADHD **i**n children. **T**he main **th**ings are:

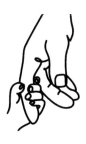

Help your **ch**ild to **und**erstand ADHD.
1. **AD**HD is **n**ot a **fl**aw! Everyone **h**as things **th**at make **u**s all **bri**lliantly unique... **ex**plain that **o**ne of **t**he special **th**ings about **t**hem is **th**at their **br**ain works **dif**ferently!

2. **Li**nk it **t**o their **str**engths! ADHD **c**an often **be** described **as** a '**sup**erpower', is **yo**ur child **su**per intuitive? **D**o they **wo**rk in a creative **w**ay, and **ta**ckle problems **fr**om a **dif**ferent approach?

3. **Ex**plain that **i**n addition **t**o these **gr**eat things, **i**t can **al**so mean **th**at they **mi**ght struggle **t**o concentrate **a**t times, **o**r struggle **t**o stay **st**ill... and **th**at is **com**pletely fine!!

Get the **ri**ght support **be**yond an **AD**HD diagnosis.
1. **In**volve your **ch**ild's Pre-School **o**r School. **T**here is **lo**ts of **tai**lored support **t**hey can **p**ut in **p**lace to **he**lp your **ch**ild learn **i**n a **w**ay that **wo**rks for **t**hem!

2. **Jo**in support **gr**oups to **le**arn more **ab**out ADHD, **t**o share **expe**riences and **t**o get **su**pport from **ot**hers in **t**he same **pos**ition as **y**ou!

3. **Va**rious studies **sh**ow that **exe**rcise can **be** a **ga**me changer **f**or helping **chi**ldren and **ad**ults with **AD**HD to **ma**nage their **sym**ptoms. According **t**o Child **Mi**nd Institute (**https://chi**ldmind.org/article/adhd-**a**nd-**exe**rcise) "as **li**ttle as **hal**f an **ho**ur a **d**ay of **exe**rcise can **he**lp kids — **esp**ecially younger **on**es — focus (**a**nd feel) **be**tter".

About the Author

Stevie lives **b**y the **Se**aside in **Es**sex with **h**er husband **a**nd three **wond**erfully boisterous **so**ns.

She writes **p**a**r**t-**ti**me, alongside a career **i**n learning **a**nd development. **Wh**en she **i**sn't running **ar**ound with **h**er boys, **y**ou can **us**ually find **h**er writing **i**n the **co**mfort of **h**er home **of**fice - **al**ways with a cup **o**f coffee **a**nd a **c**at on **h**er lap!

Acknowledgements

Following on from my first book in this collection 'Scarlett the Turtle', I went into the production of this book with so much excitement and added confidence. That is really thanks to everyone who supported and celebrated the release of Scarlett the Turtle - thank you all so much!

Special mention goes to my beautiful niece Poppy, who was the inspiration for this book. Also my three son's Oliver, Harvey and Jude - the drive and passion behind everything do. To my husband Lyndon - thank you for your unwavering support!!

Last but not least, my biggest thanks of all once again goes to all of you, my cherished readers! The thought of children and their grown ups reading this book together still feels like a dream. From the bottom of my heart - thank you!